SAFETY TOWN ®

Playing on the Playground

By Dorothy Chlad

Illustrations by Lydia Halverson

CHILDRENS PRESS ®

CHICAGO

Safety Town is a comprehensive educational program that introduces safety awareness and preventive procedures to preschool children. During the twenty-hour course, children learn—through their own involvement—safety rules about fire, poison, strangers, traffic, home, train, car, bus, playground, animals, toys, etc. They participate in safety activities in the indoor classroom and practice safety lessons on the outdoor layout, which consists of a miniature town complete with houses, sidewalks, and crosswalks. Role-playing in simulated and real-life situations, under the guidance of a teacher and uniformed personnel, provides children with learning experiences. This allows them to respond properly when confronted with potentially dangerous situations that occur in everyday life.

National Safety Town Center, established in 1964, is the pioneer organization dedicated to promoting preschool-early childhood safety education. This nonprofit organization has been largely responsible for enlightening the media, corporations, government officials, and the general public to the importance of safety education for children. Its network of dedicated volunteers continually supports and promotes the importance of safety for children through the Safety Town program.

For more information about
the Safety Town program
please contact
  National Safety Town Center
  P.O. Box 39312
  Cleveland, Ohio 44139
  216-831-7433

Library of Congress Cataloging-in-Publication Data

Chlad, Dorothy.
    Playing on the playground.

    (Safety Town)
    Summary: Jackie and her friends play at the play-
ground, always obeying the safety rules.
    [1.   Playgrounds—Safety measures—Fiction.
2. Safety—Fiction] I. Halverson, Lydia, ill.
II. Title. III. Series: Chlad, Dorothy. Safety Town.
PZ7.C4457P1   1987   [E]   87-5197
ISBN O-516-O1989-9

Childrens Press, Chicago

Hi, my name is Jackie.
I am going to the
playground.

I always go with
my friends.

I NEVER go alone.

There are so many things
at the playground.

I have fun.

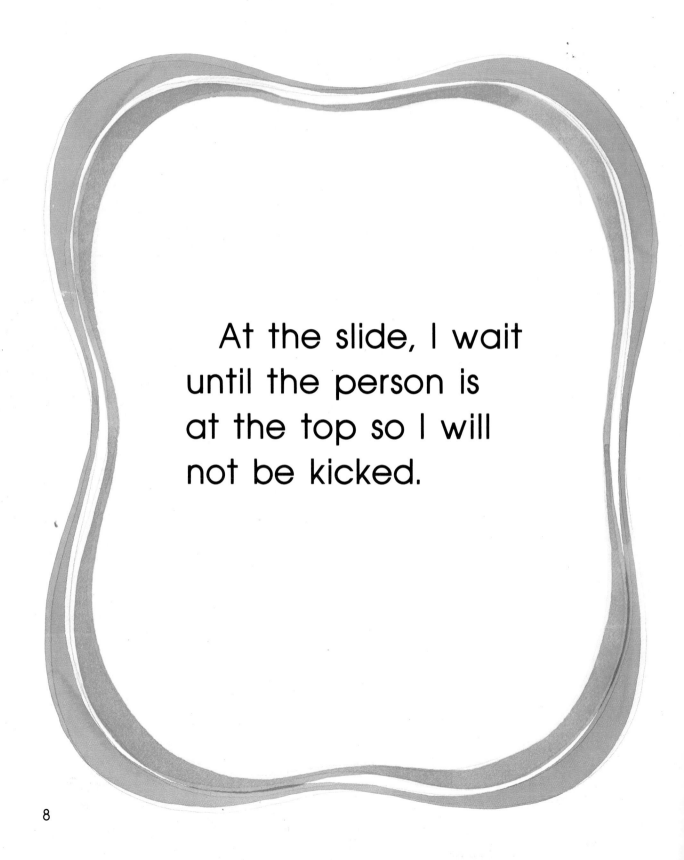

At the slide, I wait
until the person is
at the top so I will
not be kicked.

9

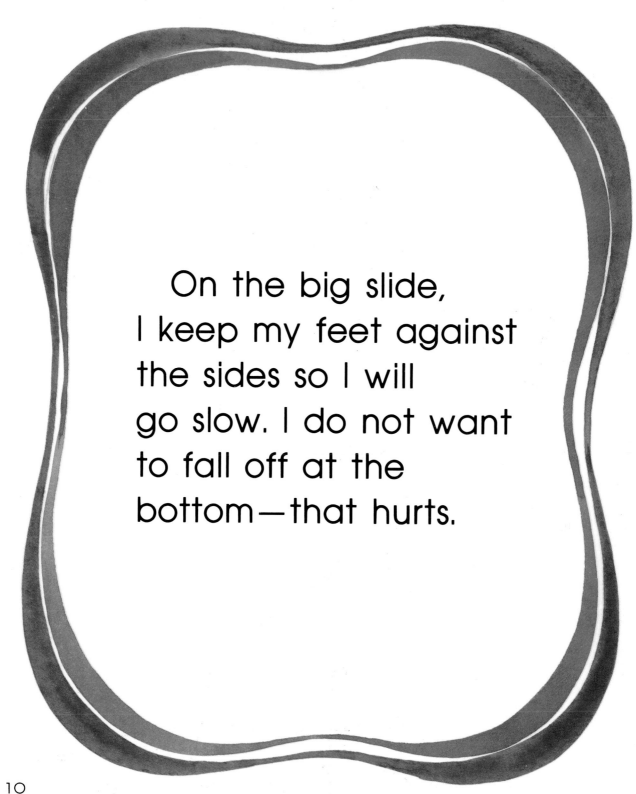

On the big slide,
I keep my feet against
the sides so I will
go slow. I do not want
to fall off at the
bottom—that hurts.

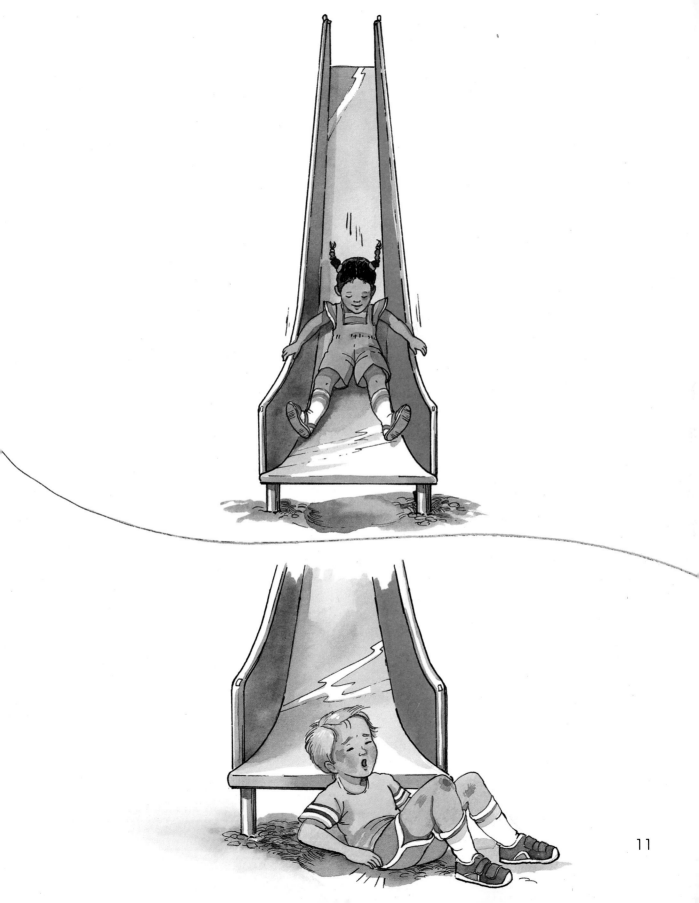

On the small slide,
I keep my feet together
and go faster.

When I go to the swings,
I always walk in front.
I do not want to get hit.

When I get off the swings, I walk in front, too.

One day my friend
Leslie ran in front
of the swings. She
got hurt.

19

I pump the swing myself. Mom pushes my brother.

The boxes are fun.
Sometimes we all
play together. We
must be careful.

The merry-go-round
goes fast. I ALWAYS
hold on tight.

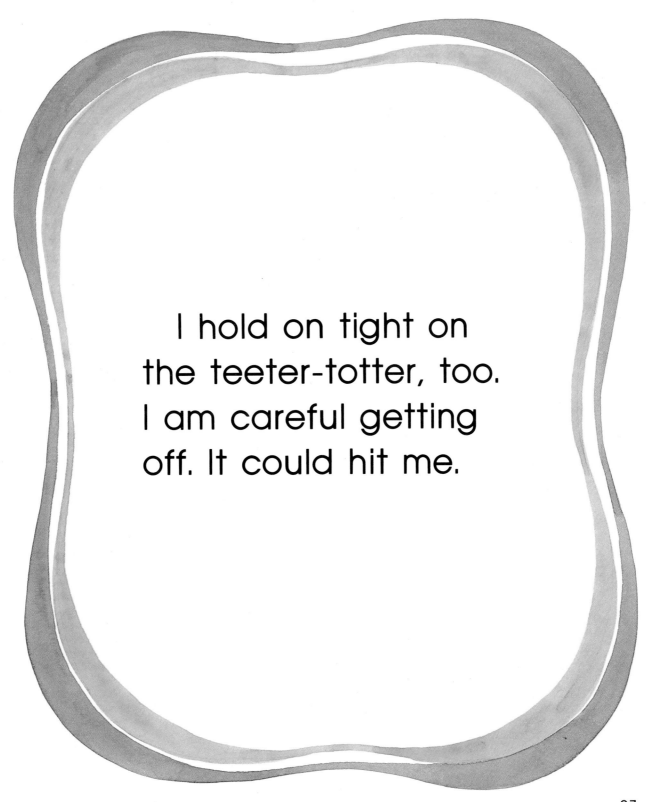

I hold on tight on
the teeter-totter, too.
I am careful getting
off. It could hit me.

Your playground might have different things.

Have your mom or dad
tell you their playground
rules so you will not
get hurt.

Remember my rules.
Then you, too, can have
fun at the playground.

1. NEVER go alone

2. ALWAYS go with friends

3. DO NOT walk in front of moving swings

4. Wait at the bottom of the slide

5. ALWAYS hold on tight

6. Be careful—Be alert

About the Author

Dorothy Chlad, founder of the total concept of Safety Town, is recognized internationally as a leader in Preschool/Early Childhood Safety Education. She has authored eight books on the program, and has conducted the only workshops dedicated to the concept. Under Mrs. Chlad's direction, the National Safety Town Center was founded to promote the program through community involvement.

She has presented the importance of safety education at local, state, and national safety and education conferences, such as National Community Education Association, National Safety Council, and the American Driver and Traffic Safety Education Association. She serves as a member of several national committees, such as the Highway Traffic Safety Division and the Educational Resources Division of National Safety Council. Chlad was an active participant at the Sixth International Conference on Safety Education.

Dorothy Chlad continues to serve as a consultant for State Departments of Safety and Education. She has also consulted for the TV program. "Sesame Street" and recently wrote this series of safety books for Childrens Press.

A participant of White House Conferences on safety, Dorothy Chlad has received numerous honors and awards including National Volunteer Activist and YMCA Career Woman of Achievement in 1983, Dorothy Chlad received the **President's Volunteer Action Award** from President Reagan for twenty years of Safety Town efforts. In 1986 Cedar Crest College in Pennsylvania presented her with an honorary degree, Doctor of Humane Letters. She has also been selected for inclusion in **Who's Who of American Women**, the **Personalities of America**, the **International Directory of Distinguished Leadership, Who's Who of the Midwest**, and the 8th Edition of **The World Who's Who of Women.**

About the Artist

Lydia Halverson was born Lydia Geretti in midtown Manhattan. When she was two, her parents left New York and moved to Italy. Four years later her family returned to the United States and settled in the Chicago Area. Lydia attended the University of Illinois, graduating with a degree in fine arts. She worked as a graphic designer for many years before finally concentrating on book illustration.